WILDLIFE HOSPITAL

Jaws the Hedgehog
and other stories

First published in Great Britain by
Collins in 1995

1 3 5 7 9 8 6 4 2

Collins is a division of
HarperCollins*Publishers* Ltd,
77-85 Fulham Palace Road,
Hammersmith, London W6 8JB

Text copyright © Les Stocker 1995
Photographs copyright © Les Stocker 1995

The author asserts the moral right to be
identified as the author of the work.

Printed and bound in Great Britain
by HarperCollins Manufacturing Ltd, Glasgow

ISBN 0 00 675181 4

St. Tiggywinkles Wildlife Hospital

Jaws the Hedgehog and other stories

Les Stocker

Collins
An Imprint of HarperCollins*Publishers*

Contents

Introduction

These stories tell of the bravery of some of the fifteen thousand animals and birds who arrive at St. Tiggywinkles Wildlife Hospital each year. Sue, my wife, Colin, my son, and I, together with all our staff and volunteers, do all we can to get these patients better and released back to the wild.

Every animal or bird will fight for its life and, given half a chance, will fight to get better. The animals in this book are real animals who we have been lucky to know. But I have turned their experiences into stories, which I love to tell. I hope that you enjoy reading them and meeting some of the animals that make my life worth living.

People at St. Tiggywinkles

Les, Sue and Colin Stocker	Founders and Directors
Dr John Lewis	Specialist veterinary consultant
Peter Kertesz	Animal dentist
Jo Knibb	Head veterinary nurse
Lisa Frost	New admissions nurse
Lia Titman	Junior veterinary nurse
Jane Ravie	Junior veterinary nurse
Matt Dodds	Rescue coordinator

Plus dozens of volunteers

Jaws the Hedgehog

St. Tiggywinkles is a hospital for wild animals and birds. It's in the countryside not far from London. Just like hospitals for humans, patients of all shapes and sizes arrive for treatment throughout the day and night. Jaws, a baby hedgehog, arrived wrapped in tissue paper and hidden in an old biscuit tin.

"Squeak, squeak, squeak," went the little bundle of tissue paper. As I unwrapped it I found something that looked more like half a pork sausage than a baby animal. Its bright pink skin, with just a few floppy white spines, suggested to me that it was only one or two days old. Like many baby animals, its eyes and ears had not opened and I knew that they wouldn't do so for another couple of weeks. But the baby hedgehog, despite its tiny size, already had a very loud voice and its urgent squeaking let everyone at St. Tiggywinkles know that it wanted feeding.

The tiny hedgehog had been discovered by a soppy Cavalier spaniel with floppy ears called Toby. It had lost its family somehow and was wandering around squeaking a loud noise that seemed to say, "I want my mum and I want some food."

Toby had picked it up from under some bushes and put it on to his owner Katie Jones' foot as she was playing in the garden. It was lucky Katie heard the hedgehog squeaking or she might have trodden on it. Katie's mum brought him to the hospital straight away.

The little urchin (which means baby hedgehog) was so young I couldn't tell if it was a boy or girl. But as he was so noisy he seemed just like a naughty little boy. When he grew older I would be able to find out if I was right or wrong.

As I picked him up I realized that something was terribly wrong with the tiny animal. His mouth hung open and his little pink tongue was waving about in the air. When Toby first picked him up he must have accidentally injured the little urchin and he seemed to have broken his bottom jaw. This meant that he wouldn't be able to feed. If he couldn't close his mouth he wouldn't be able to swallow the goats' milk we would give him. That's why I decided to call the little fella 'Jaws'!

Jaws didn't have a mum to look after him, so we knew that unless we kept him warm and fed him he would die.

"Squeak, squeak, squeak." Jaws didn't care about what we were thinking – all he wanted was food. We had to work out a way to fix the broken jaw so that he could drink his milk. Dr John, our vet, would use wire and screws to mend an adult hedgehog's jaw, but our little urchin was too small for this – and he was HUNGRY!

I called Sue – she's an expert at feeding all baby wild animals. Sue was the first person to work out that baby hedgehogs liked goats' milk. (Just as well because can you imagine trying to get hedgehog milk by milking a rolled-up mother hedgehog? No way!)

"I've got an idea," I said to Sue. "As his eyes and ears are still closed, why don't I put some sticky-plaster around his head to hold his jaw closed."

"But I still won't be able to feed him," answered Sue, trying to quieten the little urchin down.

"Yes you will. If I leave a little gap at the front— " I never finished. Sue knew what the rest of my idea was. "I can put the milk in so that he can swallow," she interrupted, jumping up and bringing the urchin to me so that I could try it out.

Sue held Jaws up so that I could lift his little

broken jaw and wrap the sticky-plaster round his head to keep his mouth nearly closed. It seemed to work. We would leave the tape on until his eyes opened in about twelve days' time. By then the broken bones would have had enough time to mend.

Sue offered Jaws the first few drops of goats' milk. "Come on, little fella," she whispered as she held Jaws in the palm of her hand. "Try some of this. It'll make you feel much better."

Gently and slowly she pushed the soft rubber tip of the bottle into the tiny gap at the front of the sticky-plaster. At first Jaws didn't know what to do. He coughed and spluttered and soon had milk everywhere, as well as coming down his nose.

"Come on. You can do better than that," Sue tried to encourage him. Suddenly Jaws got the hang of it and swallowed the first few drops. Then there was no stopping him as he drank down milk from five tiny bottles!

"That's enough, greedyguts," said Sue, "you'll burst if you have any more."

Jaws now looked like a little pink balloon. He had a big round tummy and, like all babies who gulp their food down, he had wind and started to squeak all over again, kicking his legs as though he had a rotten tummy ache.

Sue laid him over her shoulder, just like mums do with human babies. She patted and rubbed his back with her finger. "Come on then. Let's have a good burp."

Jaws seemed to like this and kicked out his little back legs that now looked like the legs of a tiny, tiny baby elephant. He hiccuped a little burp and seemed to feel much better. He had actually stopped squeaking, too.

But he didn't keep quiet for long. Minutes later, he piped up again. "Ooh, we are a noisy little baby," said Sue. "After all that milk I think he needs a wee."

Baby animals cannot go to the toilet by themselves. In the wild their mothers lick them to make them go. (I was sure Sue was not going to do that!) She had to use a damp cotton bud so that the little urchin would think his mother was licking him.

Jaws loved this. He pushed his little pink back legs straight out then pushed drop after drop of wee into the bowl Sue had put underneath him. He even stopped squeaking and I am sure he would have smiled if his mouth had not been taped up!

After all this activity Jaws was soon ready to go to sleep until his next feed in two hours' time. His bed was in a very warm hospital cage. It had a glass front so that we could watch him moving round to see if he came out looking for food.

Sue had wrapped him in a soft blue towel and had given him a toy koala bear to cuddle up to just in case he felt lonely without his mum. He soon fell fast asleep, flat on his back. He must have been dreaming for his four little legs were kicking in the air. Perhaps he was dreaming of that terrible time when Toby first picked him up.

Then two hours later – "Squeak! squeak! squeak!" Jaws had woken up and wanted feeding again.

After he was ten days old he started to take a lot more milk and let Sue have three hours off between each feed. Sue was very tired after all this and was more pleased than anyone when the day came to remove his sticky-plaster to see if his broken jaw had healed.

Jaws looked a lot different now. Most of his white spines had gone and brown ones had grown in their place. He now looked like a hedgehog. Sue held him up for me to take his tape off. But as soon as I took hold of the first corner he curled up into a ball. He could smell that I was a stranger. He knew I wasn't Sue, who was like a mum to him because she had always given him his milk.

It took ages and ages to get the tape off. Every time a little hair or whisker got stuck to it Jaws would curl into a ball and I would have to wait for him to unroll.

Slowly and carefully I unstuck the tape. I had to take even more care where the tape covered his eyes which were still closed. When all the tape was off Jaws seemed to be able to hold his mouth up. Hooray! His jawbone seemed to have knitted together. Jaws was better.

Next I took a cotton bud and dunked it in some warm water to see if I could open up his eyes. As I gently wiped it over his eyelids the first little black button eye opened and Jaws could see, for the first time, the strange human world he was growing up in. When both eyes were open Sue took him away and cuddled him.

"There, there. Did the nasty man pull your whiskers out? How about some nice warm milk for such a brave boy?"

Sue gave Jaws his first feed since the sticky-tape had been taken off. It had worked, and for the first time Jaws even managed to smack his lips as all other hedgehogs do.

Now, with his eyes open, Jaws found a whole new world and soon started to explore his new bigger hospital cage. He even started self-lathering – that's when a hedgehog goes all silly and starts to bend backwards putting spit all over his spines. We don't know why hedgehogs do this but young as he was Jaws definitely knew and was soon in a very fine mess.

A week later and Jaws had started to grow his first teeth. Just like human babies when they are teething, these were sore so Sue rubbed baby teething gel onto his gums. But not even teething stopped him guzzling loads and loads of milk at each feed. Sue decided it was time to teach him to feed himself.

She put into his cage shallow bowls of goats' milk for him to lap just like a cat. Jaws took some time to catch on and at first kept walking through the bowls covering himself and his cage in sticky milk! Then he accidentally tasted some of his paddling pool of milk and started to lap, and lap, and lap. Jaws was a messy little eater, and Sue always had to give him a good wash down with baby wipes after his dinner. But Jaws was learning too. He could already go to the toilet by himself and didn't need the damp cotton buds any more. Jaws was growing up – fast!

After Jaws showed that he could lap goats' milk the time came to give him proper solid food and that was when he got really messy. All the urchins at St. Tiggys are fed on a sticky, gooey mess we call Hedgehog Glop. We blend together dried insects, water and vitamins until it looks like soft, brown ice cream. Once the little hedgehogs get used to it they love it. I sometimes think they like playing in it as much as eating it.

Jaws certainly thought it was a new game and jumped straight into his first bowl of Glop. He rolled in it, he stamped it all round his cage, he had it all over his face and even self-lathered himself so that he had it all over his spines too. He did everything with it – except eat it.

Sue had seen all this before with umpteen other urchins. She had an answer and sprinkled a little goats' milk on the top of the next bowl of Glop. Jaws soon recognized his old favourite and started to lap the milk. Suddenly, he stopped. He had lapped up a big lump of Glop. He smacked his lips.

"Cor, this is good," he seemed to say, and dived in and ate half a bowl. When he had finished he stood in the bowl and did his toilet. Then he muckily walked off to go to sleep with his toy koala.

But Sue saw him sneak off and grabbed him. She gave him a good wash even though he kept rolling into a ball and making himself mucky, all over again.

Jaws ate lots and lots of Glop and grew very strong. All his new teeth came through so we persuaded him to eat normal dog food which was not as mucky as Glop. He was not allowed any more milk. We knew that this would give him – and all grown-up hedgehogs – a bad tummy!

* * *

At ten weeks Jaws was already as big as some of these grown-up hedgehogs. He turned out to be quite a naughty teenager. His jaw was better, he had all his teeth and he seemed to have developed a liking for nipping, and biting – the little scallywag! Perhaps he remembered the time that Toby the dog had picked him up in his big, drooly mouth. Now he would like to bite Toby back.

When we tried to introduce him to other young hedgehogs, he would crawl up by the side of them and, when we were not looking, he would bite them in the soft skin just above their front legs. He would not let go until their screams called us to the rescue and we had to pull him off.

Jaws had grown up very early and like adult hedgehogs he wanted to be on his own. He didn't like other hedgehogs, and judging by the bites his broken jaw seemed to have completely healed. Jaws had grown from the naughty little boy we first took in to a biting machine with teeth. As well as biting any other hedgehogs he met he soon took to biting anybody who got in his way. He regularly bit me as I weighed him and made one of the nurses squeal by nipping the edge of her ear as she checked his toenails. And he'd even had a go at a Member of Parliament who was on a goodwill visit to St. Tiggywinkles.

But his greatest moment and the final crunch came when I took him to appear on TV. We'd been asked with Jaws to a TV studio to talk about our work at St. Tiggys, along with a very glamorous American movie star who had never seen a hedgehog.

"Oh, isn't he cute," the actress said. She was obviously taken in by his pretty face.

Then she asked to hold him. Jaws was not impressed and promptly clamped his jaws around her finger which was dripping with diamond rings.

"Eeek," she screamed at the camera trying to shake Jaws off her finger now dripping with blood. I took Jaws from her but he immediately clamped on to my finger. Since the show had to go on I tried to keep smiling at the camera.

Afterwards, I said to Sue, "That's it. This hedgehog is ready to be released. He needs to be back in the wild, biting slugs not humans. It's time to go, Jaws."

We found him a home in a very large garden where he could come and go as he pleased. It was a little like the garden Toby had first found him in. We built him a special wooden hedgehog house and even put his koala in it to keep him company. But Jaws was as stroppy as ever and chose to live in an old black plastic sack by the compost heap rather than in the new house we had built him.

He is still up to his old tricks and on some warm nights you can hear the screams of other hedgehogs as they come too near his patch.

Jaws has really learnt to bite back!

A Wildcat Goes to the Dentist

Some animal patients at St. Tiggys are much more difficult to handle than others. We have treated snakes, lizards, turtles and even a wallaby, but none has been as wild as the unexpected visitor we took in from Scotland.

The phone rang one Sunday evening and I expected the usual animal emergency – a fox, badger or even a deer. But this was different and surprisingly came from a friend of mine, Beatrice Brinkler, who looks after wild animals in the north of Scotland. Beatrice told me that the week before a man called John McPhee had been driving along an isolated road in Scotland in a terrible storm. He had slowly eased his sleek car through the wild rain that was lashing through the horrible, dark February night. As he wiped the mist from the inside of his windscreen he suddenly caught just a glimpse of two electric green eyes glaring at him in the dimness of his headlights. A chill ran up his back and he slammed on his brakes. But too late. The dull thud from the other side of the car told him that he had hit whatever it was he saw in his headlights.

For a moment he sat there, hardly daring to move. But he had to look. Shaking, he slid over to the passenger seat and wiped the glass but the sleet outside stopped him seeing more than just a few centimetres into the darkness. He pressed the button to lower the electric window and as it opened the wind screamed in. An icy blast of sleet hit him full in the face. He fumbled in the glove compartment to find the old torch his uncle had given him many years before. He banged it to make it work and shone its weak yellow light into the gloomy unknown outside.

He could just about see the white line and was shocked to see that he had been driving on the wrong side of the road and was now stopped facing the wrong way. He only hoped that his flashing hazard warning lights would be seen by any other cars coming along.

He was scared, but he had to get out and see what he had hit. Bending over to try and stand up in the wind he started to look round behind the car.

In the dark by his feet he saw the two electric green eyes reflecting in his torch. He breathed a big sigh of relief as he saw that the creature was not a phantom of the night but a big, tabby cat lying there in the wet.

He knelt down in the wet, to see if the poor cat was still alive. There was blood coming from its mouth and it certainly looked dead as it lay there being soaked by the storm. He took off his driving glove and felt under the cat's leg. It was cold as if it was dead but through his numb fingers he could feel a heartbeat.

"Thank heavens you are alive," he muttered to the unconscious cat. "Let's get you in the car and get you looked after."

The cat was still unconscious as John laid it on the back seat of the car. It was a huge cat, nearly as long as the seat and very heavy. John decided to drive to Ullapool where he knew Beatrice would be able to help.

In the storm it took two hours to drive the twenty-five miles to Ullapool and by the time he pulled up at Beatrice's it was already way past midnight.

As soon as Beatrice saw the animal, she realized that this was no ordinary cat – it was a wildcat! She examined the still unconscious animal.

"It seems to have damaged its jaw," she said. Beatrice had never handled a wildcat before. She knew that it was much like an ordinary cat so she thought that her vet could put pieces of stainless steel wire in the broken jaw to hold it together until it healed. Then the cat would need food, water and doses of medicine every day, just like any patient. "But," said Beatrice continuing the story, "as soon as he had had his treatment he started to act just like a wildcat. When anybody went near his cage he would snarl and rush forward as though he was going to attack. Nobody could go anywhere near the cage and even when a bowl of water was slipped in, he would knock it over. It's been going on for five days and the wildcat hasn't had any food or water and, worst of all, no medicine."

Beatrice's voice softened towards the end of the call. She explained that the cat was getting weaker and if something was not done soon he would eventually die.

"Can you help us out?" she asked.

I knew that the only way to keep the cat alive was to get it to St. Tiggys where our vet, Dr John Lewis, who was a specialist on all wildcats, could give him the best attention he could possibly have.

"Of course," I said immediately, "get him down here as soon as possible."

The wildcat was driven the hundreds of miles to St. Tiggywinkles in a fast car. When he arrived I asked the driver how the pussycat was.

"That's no pussycat," he said. "That's a tiger in pussycat clothing."

I lifted the tailgate of the car and took my first look at the wildcat in his cage. I did not see much but an angry "s-s-s-s" and the bang on the front of the cage made me jump back, knocking my head on the tailgate in my rush to get out of the way.

I leant once more into the back of the car to slide the cage out. The hissing and banging carried on but this time, I didn't jump. At last I saw him, just a large tabby cat with big, green eyes and large gleaming teeth and claws.

"Come on, P. C., you are all puff and wind," I said bravely as the latest thump nearly caught my fingers holding the cage.

"Why P. C.?" asked Sue, coming out to help me with the other side of the cage. "That's not much of a name for a wildcat."

"Oh but it is," I replied, "P. C. stands for pussycat which is, after all, what he is."

As he hissed, growled and thumped, we carried P. C. through to a special quiet ward which we had set up just for him. In the room, with the door shut, it was my job to get P. C. out of his travelling cage and into a special stainless steel cage we had prepared with a nice box in one corner where he could hide away.

I put on some extra thick gloves and reached into the travelling cage to try to get hold of P. C.

Whack! One punch from his right paw, with all the claws out, tore the glove off my hand and in a flash he was then going for my bare hands. Luckily I managed to get my hand out and the lid slammed shut before he could get me.

"Right, pussycat," I told him, "if that's the way you want it I am going to have to use a grasper."

Of course, he didn't know what a grasper was.

(A grasper is a long pole, about a metre long, with a loop at one end that you slide over the animal's head. I have to use it a lot to handle badgers, foxes and otters and it does them no harm and makes moving them so much easier.)

I opened his cage slightly and slid the grasper in. Whack! I felt the full strength of his punch as he hit the grasper. But I held on and quickly slipped the loop over his head and pulled him out of the cage.

He spat, he snarled and tried to claw me. I almost threw him into his new cage and slammed the door. He was round in a flash but the door held him. I was completely out of breath and just managed to slip in a bowl of water before staggering out into the corridor. I had installed a small camera that showed pictures on a monitor in another room. This meant that we could see him without him seeing us. I also turned all the lights out except for one red light bulb. Cats are colour blind, so with only red light P. C. would think he was alone, in the dark – just what wildcats like best.

That first night we watched him. He must have been very tired because he just went into his box, curled up and went to sleep.

In the morning it was different – P. C. was wide awake and soon let us know by growling that he was not going to let anybody near his cage. I had to give him his medicine by an injection from a syringe at the end of a long pole. With everything ready I went up to his cage.

"Right, P. C.," I said trying to sound brave, "it's you or me."

"Psss! Grrr!" Whack! P. C. let me know what he thought of that.

I opened his cage just a little bit and slid my pole towards his back leg where I was going to give the injection.

Whack! He knocked the pole clean out of the box.

I tried again.

Whack! And again. Whack! But this time I carried on and carefully injected him in the leg.

Dr John had told us to put a little bit of sedative in with his treatment. This would not only help him relax but would also make him feel more like eating.

It helped us as well by letting me give P. C. his medicine every day without too many punch-ups although he did overturn every bowl of food we put in with him. He was like a child having a terrible temper tantrum.

P. C. just wouldn't settle – perhaps he was homesick. He was used to living in the cold mountains of Scotland so maybe our hospital was too warm for him. I turned all his heating off and opened the window in the room. We also made him up a litter tray full of dark brown peat, the sort of soil he would be used to in his mountain home.

We sat back and watched him on the monitor. As soon as we were out of the room he crept out and sniffed the peat. He rubbed his nose in it leaving some stuck to his white whiskers. Then he stood in it. Then he sat in it and seemed to go to the toilet.

"At last," he seemed to say to himself, "no humans round to annoy me."

"All we want you to do now, is eat," I said to myself.

P. C. didn't quite eat but for the first time we saw him lap some of the water. He then threw all his bowls around and went back into his box.

For three days we went through this routine until on the fifth day after he arrived we saw him lap his liquid food. First he sniffed it and put his nose in it. Then he licked it off his nose and seemed to like it. Then he drank about half of it. Then he threw all his bowls around again as if to say, "I only drank it to keep you happy."

The following week P. C. was to be given a full examination by Dr John and this time he had to have an injection to make him sleep.

Dr John looked at every part of P. C. He tested each leg and pushed out those fearsome claws to see if they were damaged. With a very bright small torch he looked into P. C.'s ears and into his green eyes. He felt his tummy and listened to his chest through a stethoscope. He took some blood samples and even checked the broken whiskers damaged in the car accident. Then he very carefully opened the wildcat's mouth making sure that his fingers were well out of the way.

"Oh no," he said, "he's broken some of his teeth. No wonder he's always in a temper and doesn't want to eat – he's got toothache. He will have to go to the dentist!"

Peter Kertesz was a very famous dentist who worked one day a week on animals. He always did the teeth on all our badgers and foxes.

On the morning that Peter was due to come, P. C. needed another injection to make him sleep. He didn't like this and spat and snarled as Dr John gave it to him. But after a couple of minutes P. C.'s head started to wobble and he sat down and fell over fast asleep. Dr John picked him up like a baby and carried him through into the operating theatre. Peter was waiting with all his instruments laid out on a shiny hospital trolley.

"Bzzz, whirr," went the drill rising to a high pitched scream as it cut away the dead parts of that first tooth.

I could smell the burning that I knew so well from my visits to the dentist. I was glad I was only watching.

P. C. had to have four fillings and one tooth taken out. An animal's bite is very powerful and the repairs have to be very strong. When he woke up he was given some painkillers but after two days he was eating twice as much as normal and when he snarled he seemed to have bigger teeth than ever!

So P. C. was nearly as good – or bad – as new.

But sadly, when he analysed P. C.'s blood samples, Dr John discovered that he had a blood disease that could easily be caught by other wildcats. He had probably caught it off an ordinary cat while in Scotland. (This is one of the reasons why we say that wild animals should never be kept with pets like dogs and cats.)

P. C. would always be able to spread the disease so he could never be released. It would probably not make him ill but it did mean that he could not even go into a zoo and live with other wildcats.

We don't want P. C. to be lonely so we'll search all over Britain for a wildcat friend who has the same condition.

P. C. is still a wild wildcat – that's his nature – but now he's been to the dentist and no longer has toothache, he's a lot less grumpy. We will find him a friend in the end.

Eric the Red –
the Bad-tempered Deer

All human rescue services – fire, police and ambulance – have an emergency 999 phone line. St. Tiggywinkles has its own emergency line where people can call when they find a large animal needing our help.

One urgent call came in just as I was having my early evening tea break. This was no normal call and led to me struggling with the biggest, meanest animal St. Tiggys had ever seen.

The caller had said that there was a deer trapped in the field next to her house. The house was in a small village about twenty miles from the hospital. I knew the area very well and guessed that the animal was a fallow deer – the largest wild animal in this area. Unfortunately, Matt, who I always take with me to help me with big animals, was already out rescuing a duck with fishing line caught around its legs. He had taken our main rescue vehicle with emergency lights, first-aid equipment and a mobile telephone. Our other car wasn't really big enough to carry a large deer and could have got stuck if we had to drive across fields. Still, it had to do so I loaded it up with any rescue equipment I could find around the hospital.

There wasn't much: a few deer masks – these are made of cloth and cover a deer's head to keep it quiet; some blankets and some sedatives – medicines to help to quieten the deer just in case it was too big and dangerous to handle.

Lisa, one of our nurses, came with me so that she could drive us back if I had to sit with the deer to control it.

We reached the village and found the field. There was a mass of trees at the end of it. I couldn't see the deer but grabbed an armful of blankets and a mask and climbed the fence into the field.

When we saw the deer we stopped dead in our tracks. This was no ordinary deer, it was the biggest fallow buck I had ever seen. His fur was jet black and on top of his head were a set of antlers that looked as if they could make mincemeat of anybody who got in their way. He was about one and half metres tall at the shoulder and must have weighed 100 kilos. This was far heavier than me, even after a large Christmas dinner! He was roaring and thrashing his antlers, which were trapped in rope tied to the thick branch of a tree. Some children must have been using it as a Tarzan swing. The deer seemed to be making the whole wood shake in terror.

And I had to rescue him.

I moved towards him on my own and stopped still. His big eyes rolled to show white against the black of his fur. He snorted at me and stamped his front feet. I am sure he would have tried to kill me if he had not been tied by the rope that was wound round his antlers. If I cut the rope from his antlers he would be free, but as he was so angry he might attack me. I wondered if I would be able to climb the tree fast enough to get out of his way.

I walked round him slowly and my heart sank. One of his back legs seemed to be dangling and not moving. In his struggles he must have broken his leg. I now knew that I could not just let him go, I would have to take him back for treatment.

Then I heard a scream from Lisa. Rushing across the field was a man with a rifle in his hand. It was the ranger aiming his gun at the deer who was now more frightened than ever and pounding the ground making his broken leg even worse.

"Stand back," the ranger bellowed. "I'm going to shoot that animal."

"Oh no you're not," said Lisa getting between him and the deer.

"Get out of the way, you stupid girl." He was now getting angry.

I rushed over and shouted at him. "You've got no rights over here and you are not going to shoot anything." I was shaking and could hear my heart pounding in my ears.

He stomped off muttering something under his breath about "blooming do-gooders".

I was glad he was gone. All we had to worry about now was how to catch this deer.

I drove the car as quietly as possible as near to the deer as I could. Then I told Lisa that I would try and hold the deer still so that she could sedate him with an injection in his back leg.

I had to put a deer mask on him so that he wouldn't be frightened by what he might see. His big eyes rolled and he tossed his head and turned to face me. I could see his nose twitching as he tried to make out my scent. I don't know who was more frightened, him or me.

I walked towards him and he moved back a

bit. Great. My plan was to make him walk round and round the tree so that the rope holding him got shorter and shorter until he could move no more. I needed to be patient in case he tried to charge at me.

The plan was slowly working and when his head was tight against the trunk I grabbed hold of his antlers to stop him unwinding again.

"Quick, Lisa," I whispered urgently, "get those injections in but don't get kicked."

Lisa looked tiny creeping up to the back of the huge deer. One injection went in – the deer did not seem to notice. The second one made him jump a bit. I just about managed to hold on to his antlers as Lisa jumped out of the way.

After four injections he started to get a bit groggy and I walked him back around the tree so that he could lie down.

Twenty-five minutes later he was lying down as though he was drunk. He was not actually asleep, so as I cut the rope away from the tree I had to make sure that he did not get up behind me. When the rope was cut I let his head sink slowly to the ground and sat on him while Lisa laid a blanket next to him. The sedative would only last a short while so it was crucial that we got him in the car and to a safe place before he woke up.

Bit by bit I lifted him on to the blanket – first his back end, which was the heaviest and then his head. Even then, those big eyes still rolled back to the white as though he was about to get up and run off taking me with him.

When he was on the blanket we dragged him over to the car and somehow bundled him over the bumper and into the back. All the time we were moving him he was grumbling – it was like a deep roar from down in his chest.

It was too far to drive him back to the hospital before he woke up so I decided to take him to my friend Polly's farm which wasn't too far away.

"This must be Eric the Red," she said. "He looks like one of those old Viking warriors with a horned helmet!"

"Well, Eric the Red is about to come round, and he's not a happy Viking. Can we keep him in one of your stables?"

"Of course," Polly said, "but it's round the corner. How on earth are we going to get him in there?"

I had an idea! We would wheel him in a wheelbarrow!

Can you imagine how funny we must have looked? Three people, one very heavy sleeping deer and... a rusty old wheelbarrow! Only his body would fit into the wheelbarrow and even then his bottom hung over between the handles and Lisa had to hold his head up by his antlers to stop it dragging on the floor. His legs stuck out to one side of the wheelbarrow so I got Polly to hold the broken one to stop it getting damaged any further.

When we were in the stable I just tipped him out as gently as I could. I don't think we could have lifted him again. I sat him up the right way

his mask on to keep him quiet while we
away and worked out what to do next.

We couldn't move him again so I decided
that we should line the stable with bales of hay,
to stop him hurting himself. He would stay in
the stable until his leg got better. Lisa wrapped
his leg in foam until we could get a vet to him.

The following day six of us from St. Tiggys
– including Matt and Sue – went to Polly's farm
and found Eric still with his mask on, standing
up on his three good legs just raring to do battle
with anyone that went in the stable. We knew
we would have to sedate him again, otherwise
we'd never be able to get the bales of hay into
the stable and us out again.

Eric, of course, had other ideas.

Matt went in first with me right behind him.
Sue locked the stable door behind us. Eric knew
that something was going on, for although he
could not see us through the mask, his nose was
flaring wide open as he picked up our scent. He
stamped his front feet on the ground and snorted.

St. Tiggywinkles
started out as a
shed for injured
hedgehogs.

It is now one of the most
advanced wildlife hospitals
in Britain.

Les and Sue Stocker,
founders of
St. Tiggywinkles.

Jaws has his first feed.

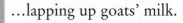

...ready to have his bandage taken off.

...lapping up goats' milk.

...being mucky with Glop!

P. C. is no ordinary cat...

...he's a tiger in pussycat clothing!

"This cat will have to go to the dentist."

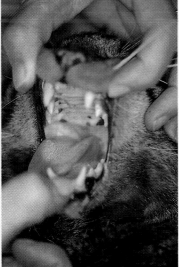

Les keeps Eric still so that Lisa can sedate the angry deer.

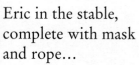

Eric in the stable,
complete with mask
and rope…

…and free
to go.

Matt looks happy – he's caught six swans.

Les gently squeezing Lectade into Bisto's mouth.

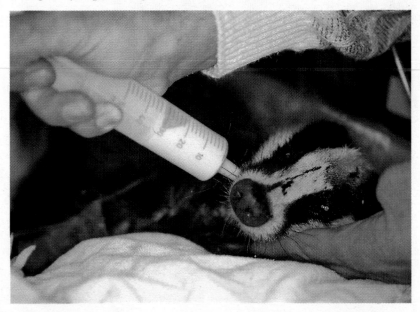

Bisto's badger
friends, and Sue!

Bottle is missing his bottle!

"We want FOOD," shout Bottle and Spot.

Baby owls in the nursery.

A nest with a difference!

A ball of fluff?
No, a baby bird.

Matt grabbed hold of both antlers to hold him still.

"Wa-a-a-gh!" Matt cried out as Eric lifted his antlers and picked Matt right off the floor.

Then he charged round with Matt lying between his antlers kicking his legs in the air.

"Whatever happens, don't let go," I shouted.

Matt hung on for his life. Finally Eric stopped charging and I jumped in to help Matt. With both of us holding the antlers we had him under control. Neither of us dared to let go, so I had to call Sue in to give Eric the sedative and then get out again.

Then to a cry of 'one, two, three!' we both let go at the same time and shot out of the door.

Eric went round and round the stable trying to find us but we were safely outside the locked door. It took about twenty minutes for the sedative to work but finally Eric sat quietly down so that we could get on with bringing in the bales of hay.

Our next job was to get a vet to look at the

broken leg. Dr John was away in Africa looking after some large monkeys called drills – an endangered species. We had to call in a local vet who unfortunately wasn't used to treating deer, and certainly not a killer deer like Eric.

The vet would not accept our offer of help even though Eric was now throwing bales of hay all around the stable.

He went in by himself and over the sounds of Eric stamping his feet and snorting we counted out loud. "One, two—"

We never got to 'three' as the vet fell out of the door and dropped his bag emptying all the bottles and things all over the yard.

I had seen enough and I knew Eric. I didn't want anyone to get hurt.

"Right. This is what we do. Matt and I will get the deer under control. And when I tell you to come in you can sedate it," I told the vet.

He was too shaken to argue.

Matt and I went in together and, using the grasper, we lassoed Eric's antlers and pulled him towards us. We could just about hold him. When we had him tightly against the bales of hay I shouted for the vet to come in.

Then when I said, 'OK,' he injected Eric in his back leg.

I waited until the vet was outside the stable then once again, 'one, two three,' Matt and I jumped clear while Eric went mad trying to kill the bales of hay.

In two minutes he was fast asleep – the vet had used a much stronger drug than us. This time we were ready with a stretcher – a very strong stretcher. Matt and I lifted Eric out of the stable and into the yard. The vet X-rayed the broken leg and set it in plaster just as doctors do to humans when they break an arm or leg. He then bundled up all his equipment and drove off in a hurry! We never saw him again.

We left Eric in Polly's stable and over the next six weeks watched him. At first he would just touch his broken leg to the ground. Then he would stand on it. Finally he could walk round as if nothing had ever happened. (If a human breaks a leg it's usually many months before they can walk again. Wild animals have to heal quickly – they may get attacked if they can't walk properly.)

All the time his leg was healing Eric stayed bad-tempered and would roar for hours on end. He regularly tore down all his hay bales and once even gashed Polly's head with his antlers as she was trying to put food in for him. We were all glad when the plaster was ready to come off his leg and we could let him go.

Once again we had to sedate him before cutting the plaster off with a hacksaw. The leg had healed perfectly – though Eric will always have an extra lump of bone just where it mended.

Eric the Red was now ready to leave. While he was still a little bit groggy from the sedative we helped him out to one of the fields at Polly's farm where there were definitely no rangers. We waited until he was wide awake and saw him walk off into his new home.

We are always a little sad when an animal leaves but we were all happy to see Eric go. Not just because he was bad-tempered and dangerous. Eric was a magnificent deer and king of all the other deer around. His place was out there roaring to every deer that the king was back.

Polly still sees Eric occasionally and she often hears his roaring as he fights with other bucks. His roars echo across the wood and valleys. He's still king in spite of having been with softy humans for a while!

Twelve Swans and a Lot of Mucky Surprises

I expect you've seen on television what happens when seabirds get covered in oil. But it isn't only seabirds that get oil on their feathers. Birds all over the country have this problem and centres like St. Tiggywinkles have to rescue and clean them.

One day Matt took a telephone call on our emergency line. "I've got a swan rescue on the River Ouse in Bedford," he said excitedly. "And it's not just one swan, there are fourteen of them and a lot of geese."

We would have to get a rescue team together.

Some of the firefighters from our local fire brigade help out in their spare time. That day, Graham was the only firefighter not on duty so we called him in – without his fire engine, of course! Matt and I loaded two cars with rescue equipment while Jo found out exactly where the oil spill was. Colin was going to come along to film the rescue for the St. Tiggywinkles television series. We loaded his car with nets and loaves of bread to catch the swans and with Post Office sacks to carry them in. (Please do not tell the Post Office!)

As we pulled up to the spot, the police directed us right down on to the riverbank amongst all the boats and people feeding the hundreds of ducks, geese and swans. The noise of quacking and shouting was incredible.

Colin jumped out first with his camera and remarked to the nearest policeman, "What's all this swanning around then?"

The policeman was not amused so I quickly introduced myself and told him of our rescue plan. Colin – a bit of a joker – soon had his camera rolling. "We're making a duckumentary," he told them.

The officer scowled!

I stood at the top of the bank trying to work out how we would manage to catch the oiled birds. Fortunately most of the swans were standing quietly well away from the water. But a pair of swans was giving swimming lessons to their one tiny baby in amongst all the rowing boats. Each time a boat went past, the big male swan would attack, hissing and raising himself up in the water. He was flapping his enormous wings which could cause anybody who got in the way a serious injury. Every time he attacked all the ducks would rush off quacking in panic. I was concerned that at any moment one of the boats would turn over. To add to this chaos there were flocks of geese running up and down the riverbank honking their disapproval at everyone.

I had to shout above the noise. "I reckon

we'll catch the swans on the bank first. The pair on the water look pretty clean to me."

Colin, camera at the ready, had to have his say. "Go on, catch that big swan. I'd love to get a good punch-up on film."

I ignored him this time and grabbed a handful of sacks which I left with Jo as three of us made our way towards the swans.

The oil on the birds seemed to be cooking oil, which was very pale. It was difficult to see just how much each bird had on it. We decided to catch them all and judge, by sniffing them, if they did need rescuing.

We got quite close before they noticed us. Then just as Matt was about to grab the first one an old woman came charging at him swinging her handbag.

"Leave them alone! You big bullies," she shouted.

Matt ducked her handbag but missed the swan who ran off to join the others. He went after another swan and splat! He slipped over in the mud, landing flat on his face behind the swans who had got away again.

Colin, between laughing and trying to keep his camera still, said to Matt, "Can we have an action replay, please!"

At that moment another swan I was chasing flapped into Colin who only just managed to hold on to the camera. The swan carried on towards one of the policeman who bent down to catch it, but was knocked straight on to his bottom – squelch.

At last Matt, still covered in mud, caught one of the swans. But it wasn't Matt's day because as he sniffed the swan's neck the swan grabbed a mouthful of his ear. He was now getting quite grumpy. "It smells just like an old chip shop," he said. "I'll take it over to Jo."

The swans ran everywhere – up the towpath, into a boathouse and one even ended up under my car. They were like a bunch of naughty school children let out to play. Thankfully we managed to stop any of them going on to the river.

We soon had all the swans in their sacks where Jo was keeping an eye on them. They looked quite comical with their heads sticking out of one end, gurgling and hissing, while their feet flapped out of the bottom of the sacks as they tried to escape. And in true swan fashion every one of them had poohed in their sacks!

"Now for the geese," I said.

"Oh goody goody, a wild goose chase," chanted Colin. Matt threw an empty sack at him.

There were lots of geese on an island in the river and they all started honking when they saw Matt and Graham land. The noise was deafening and quite a crowd of people had gathered on the bank to watch the goings-on. Luckily all the geese seemed clean and they did not have to catch any of them so Colin didn't get his wild goose chase. But he did get some more action on film because when Matt and Graham went back to their boat it had sunk with only the rope that tied it showing above the water. Matt, deciding he was already wet, jumped in and started wading back to the bank dragging the sunken boat behind him. Graham reluctantly did the same!

"Did you find any oiled fish?" Another of Colin's jokes brought a big hug from Matt which made Colin just as wet and mucky as the other two!

We finally checked out the ducks, who all looked clean, then headed back to St. Tiggywinkles. I had most of the swans in the car with me. Matt had a couple, but Colin got away without any. He was the lucky one. Although swans look very clean and beautiful when they have no oil on them, these were quite dirty and seemed to go to the toilet after every bump in the road. By the time we got back to St. Tiggys, the back of my car was like a smelly trifle. We now had to wash the oil off the swans and wash out the insides of our two cars. Don't you just love swans!

Birds' feathers are held together with

millions of little barbs and hooks which form a waterproof raincoat. If a bird gets oil on its feathers the barbs and hooks slip open allowing water to get in and the raincoat isn't waterproof any more. When waterbirds lose their waterproofing, they sink. So the oil has to be washed off in a very special way, using soft and gentle washing-up liquid in very warm water. Each bird then has to have a warm shower until all the oil and the washing-up liquid have been rinsed out. It can take two hours to wash each bird so Matt showed some of our volunteers how to do it.

They all put on plastic aprons and plastic gloves. They thought these would stop them getting wet – but they didn't know what lively, oily swans could be like!

The first swan had oil down its neck, over its front and on its head where it had been rubbing it over its feathers. It did not want a bath. It trumpeted and flapped until Matt held its wings to its side and sat it in the warm water. It squeaked but sat still. Two volunteers held the swan and Matt started to wash it.

"First," he was saying, "get the water very warm and work the washing-up liquid well into the feathers. Don't work against the lie of the feathers but follow their line. See the way they stay in shape."

The swan now looked in a worse mess than ever as the oil started to come off its feathers. It wasn't struggling at all but every now and then made a soft wheezy sound. It seemed to like the warm water.

"We wash the back of the bird first and then its wings," Matt went on. He pulled out each gigantic wing which was nearly as big as he was. "We do its sides and then its tail and then—"

He didn't say any more because as he was trying to turn the swan over to wash its tummy it kicked. Then it trumpeted. Then, worst of all, it flapped its giant wings so that a tidal wave of warm, oily, soapy water splashed out of the sink all over Matt and the two volunteers!

"How not to do it," laughed Matt trying to get the swan under control again.

They were well and truly soaked but they managed, in spite of laughing their heads off, to finish washing the swan and start rinsing off its feathers with a spray of warm water from the tap. The more you rinse a swan, the drier it becomes as its feathers get back to normal. As the oil and washing-up liquid were washing out of the feathers, the little barbs and hooks were locking back into place forming that nice raincoat that keeps the water out. This swan was getting drier as Matt and his team got wetter and wetter.

Finally it was as clean as they could get. Matt, his socks squelching in his shoes, took the swan into the next-door room where it could stand under an infra-red heat lamp to completely dry off.

It took two days to wash all the swans. Once they were all washed and dried, we put them outside on our pond so that we could be sure that they were waterproof again. After three weeks they were ready to go back to the River Ouse, once we had checked it had no more oil on it.

But there was still more mess to come.

As Matt brought over a swan to load into the car its bottom was pointing in my direction – oh no! Splat! Splat! Splat! I was covered from head to toe in swan pooh! It was in my hair, over my glasses, down my sweat shirt, all over me. Now I had to be cleaned! I stood under the hosepipe for a wash-off. Then I knew how the swans must have felt in the wash room.

I hope it's a long time before we have any more messy swans covered in oil, but at St. Tiggys, you never know what you're going to meet next!

Ah! Bisto the Badger

Night-time is often the busiest time at St. Tiggywinkles. This is when there are often emergencies with larger animals. The buzzing of the doorbell is usually the first sign of a casualty and on this night the doorbell seemed to go into panic mode.

Bzzz! Bzzz! Bzzz!

I nearly fell out of bed in my hurry to answer the front door.

Bzzz! Bzzz! it went on.

Then Brrring-g-g! I had set off the burglar alarm in my rush to stop the buzzing. I opened the front door sleepily. Standing on the porch and looking very wide awake, were two fearsome-looking ladies in brown and green combat uniforms. They had great big black shiny boots on their feet. Luckily I knew them. Sergeant Bilko and Mavis were the nicknames we used for two women who lived near by and were always out rescuing animals.

Sergeant Bilko fired out an order. "Quick! We've got a badger and he's been shot in the head!" I think Sergeant Bilko and Mavis must watch too many police programmes on the television. They always imagine that their animals have been shot, poisoned or even bombed in a dastardly plot.

Now all I needed was to calm them down and check the animal.

"Let's have a look, shall we?" I suggested.

I opened the boot of the car slowly just in case their badger was lively and decided to hurtle out taking my fingers with it.

I needn't have worried because the badger was either knocked out or, judging by his loud snores, sleeping like a baby. I could see him quite clearly in the glare of the hospital's security lights. I could also see a small trickle of blood coming from the small hole right in the middle of his forehead. "It certainly looks as if he may have been shot."

For once I agreed with them. "Let's see what an X-ray tells us. Let Sue have the details of exactly where you found him. We'll need to keep a note of this so that we can return him to his family if he gets better."

Sue looked even sleepier than me as she came into reception ready to fill in an admittance card.

"What's the date?" she asked blearily.

I left them to it and carried the badger, by the loose skin over his neck and rump, down to the prep room to give him some first-aid treatment.

The prep room is where we treat all our animals when they first come in. I needed to set up an intravenous drip just like any hospital would do for an injured human. The badger only seemed to have one wound – the one on his head – so I cleaned this up with a little disinfectant. As I did this I could feel pieces of bone moving just under the skin – he had fractured his skull. The X-ray would tell me how this had happened. If he had been shot then it would clearly show the bullet (or more likely an airgun pellet which we find in many injured animals).

He wasn't a very big badger and was hardly breathing as he lay unconscious on the X-ray table. His short stubby legs were splayed out on either side and there was a small trickle of blood running down the white stripe of his black and white marked face. He looked totally helpless.

"Ah, he does look sweet," Sue said when she came into the X-ray room.

I then had a brainwave. "We'll call him Bisto after the gravy advertisement that says, 'Ah! Bisto'."

Our poor little badger was still unconscious,

but at least he now had a name.

I took the X-rays but couldn't find any trace of a bullet or pellet so I was fairly certain that Bisto had received his injuries in a collision with a car. A small piece of broken bone had come out through the skin causing the little hole that looked like a bullet wound.

There was little more we could do at that time – it was by now four o'clock in the morning – so I tucked him into a warm cage and went back to bed.

By eight o'clock that morning, when I went to check him, he hadn't moved at all. I was afraid he was going to die. But as I looked closely at his injured head I could feel that he was looking at me.

Then I saw one of his little black eyes water and blink as if to say, "Please help me."

I spoke softly to him hoping I might make him feel better, "Oh! so you've decided to wake up, have you? I bet you've got a thumping headache."

He blinked again and tried to move his head but it would not move.

"Now! Now! Don't try and move," I told him. "I'll get you a drink. That'll be nice, won't it?"

I went to the animal kitchen and mixed Bisto a special drink called Lectade which would make him feel much better. He obviously could not lift his head so I put some of the Lectade in a plastic bottle with a long nozzle on the end and slowly squeezed some between his teeth.

Nothing. No movement at all and the Lectade came running back out of his mouth.

I tried again, and again, and again. Still nothing and his blanket was now getting very wet with all the Lectade we were spilling.

I was about to give up when I felt his pink tongue touch the end of the bottle and he swallowed the first few drops.

He seemed to feel better for those few drops and made more effort to get the next mouthful. He even opened his jaws a little bit so that I could get the bottle into his mouth more easily. But badgers have very, very strong jaws and after a few gulps he had mangled the end of my plastic bottle. Oh well, at least Bisto was drinking – we can always get more plastic bottles, but there was only one Bisto!

Over the next two weeks Bisto began to take more and more from the bottle and even began to swallow liquid food which would give him more strength. Each day he could move his head a little bit more and even started the habit of, every now and then, shaking his head as though he was trying to shake away the wound that was still on his forehead.

Every day I fed him and cleaned his wound. One day as I was feeding him he started to growl. At first I thought he was growling at me but then I realized that somebody had crept up behind me and was watching me feed Bisto. He seemed to resent this and his growl, which I had never heard before seemed to be badger talk for, 'Go away and leave us alone!'

He was definitely feeling better but the wound on his head was not healing and I could still feel the broken bones moving, as I cleaned it. Bisto needed an operation on his brain but I knew there were unfortunately not many vets who had experience of this very special surgery – especially on a wild animal.

I thought that Bisto would have to be put to sleep. But as I hand-fed him every day, I got to know him very well and could even tell what he was thinking as he blinked his little eyes at me. He was trying very hard not to be ill. He wanted to get better and every day struggled and moved his head a little bit more. He didn't want to give up and neither did I. I would try to find a vet anywhere in Britain to get the help he needed.

With the help of Dr John we phoned everyone we could think of who might be able to carry out this very special sort of operation. In the end we found a vet called Christine Thomson at the Glasgow Veterinary College, in Scotland. She liked the sound of Bisto and his fight for life. She agreed to operate if we could get Bisto to her surgery.

I told Bisto the good news and he blinked. Perhaps that was to show me that he understood. At least now he stood a chance.

We had to get Bisto to Scotland but it was a long way from the hospital. Bumpy roads, noisy motorways and long hot traffic jams wouldn't have been good for Bisto so we decided to take him by train.

The train for Glasgow left Euston Station in London at midnight. As we left for the station everybody at St. Tiggys came outside to say goodbye. Bisto gave them all a tired growl even though he knew they all loved him.

At Euston we were met by a scruffy ticket attendant whose shirt was hanging out because he could not do his belt up.

"Where are you going?" he demanded gruffly.

"Glasgow," I replied waving my tickets at him.

"What you got in there?" he asked suspiciously. "A cat?" The idea seemed to make him even more grumpy. "All animals into the luggage van," he insisted, pointin, at Bisto's Pet Voyager.

Luckily Bisto was well covered in blankets so I did not tell him it was a badger. "It's a very sick animal and we're taking it to Glasgow for an operation."

"I don't care, mate. Rules is rules, all animals have to go in the luggage van."

We pleaded but it was no good. We agreed that Sue would go into our sleeping compartment while I spent the night in the luggage van with Bisto.

Then just as the train was about to leave, a noisy crowd of football supporters came down the platform singing at the top of their voices.

"We belong to Glasgee. Dear auld Glasgee toon!"

They were definitely going to get on our train and this sent our ticket collector into a frenzy. He jumped in amongst them trying to see their tickets. They pulled his shirt, knocked his hat off and turned him round and round in the middle of them all. He had forgotten all about us so while he was occupied with the football crowd I crept along the corridor of the train on my hands and knees carrying Bisto. I knocked on our compartment door and dived in when Sue opened it.

"Quick, shut the door," I hissed at Sue.

"Oh dear," said Sue, "do you think he saw you."

"I don't think so," I replied tucking Bisto's travelling case under one of the bunks.

There was a knock, knock at the door.

I quickly threw a blanket over Bisto's case and opened the door.

"Do you want tea in the morning!"

We gasped in relief. It wasn't the ticket collector after all but our cabin steward who knew nothing about our secret animal!

Just then Bisto let out a rude noise, as

badgers often do – just like humans!

"Excuse me," said Sue sitting on the bunk right above Bisto and rubbing her tummy.

The steward just ignored it all and walked away filling in his order pad. I locked the door and we both had a good giggle as I pulled Bisto's case out to settle him for the night.

I made Bisto a comfortable bed on the little table top and tied his intravenous drip, which he still needed, to the emergency handle. I hoped he wouldn't move and stop the whole train. After a few minutes Bisto was sound asleep, snoring just to let us know he was still alive.

Eight hours later we pulled into Glasgow where the platforms were full of people hurrying to work. We wrapped Bisto once again in lots of blankets and put him back in the travelling case. At Glasgow Veterinary College we were met by a veterinary nurse who showed us the warm cage where Bisto was going to stay. We tucked him up with his own blankets and said goodbye, for the moment. He still felt strong enough to growl at Sue and the nurse but as I tucked a folded blanket under his head to hold it up he blinked at me and I wondered if I would ever see him again.

While Bisto was at the college, Sue and I had to go to a book shop in Edinburgh to give a talk about hedgehogs. All we could think about was Bisto and how he was getting on. So it seems was everybody at St. Tiggywinkles judging by the number of phone calls we got!

The following day we got the train straight back to London, then on to St. Tiggywinkles. Sue phoned Glasgow. I was much too nervous about Bisto to speak to Christine Thomson but I listened on the extension.

"He's fine," said Christine. "I operated this morning and removed a large abscess from his brain. It was a good operation and I see no reason why, given time, he should not recover. But he's not out of the woods yet – we'll have to watch him very carefully over the next few days."

I felt so relieved that I chipped in. "If he does recover will he ever be able to be released?"

The vet thought for a while. "It's difficult to say how much brain damage there has been. I think we shall have to wait at least six months to see just how well he has recovered," she said.

Every day after that, at five o'clock, Sue phoned Christine. Every day Bisto was a little bit brighter. He still growled at everybody but was getting more relaxed with the nurse who had given up all her spare time to look after him. Then one evening, about six days after we had left him in Glasgow, the phone rang and I think we knew...

It was Christine and I knew she was crying. "Les," she sobbed, "you know the way little Bisto used to shake his head."

I went cold. "Yes, he was a terror at doing that," I managed to say.

"Well," she went on, "he did it just now and a broken piece of bone in his neck cut through a blood vessel. There was nothing we could do."

I could tell she was as heartbroken as us. Sue and I held each other, trying to be brave. Bisto had been a brave badger. He had shown that it was worth having a try.

Goodbye, Bisto, we all miss you.

Birds of a Feather

It was May at St. Tiggys and all round Britain garden birds were busy building their nests and trying to feed their ever-hungry babies. Some of these babies are often naughty and fall out of their nests and some are unlucky enough to get picked on by cats or other bigger birds.

Every May, all the hedgehogs that have stayed at St. Tiggys for the winter are prepared for release. Their ward, the biggest in the hospital, is then used for orphaned baby birds and animals. The orphans need feeding all day and most of the evening so two of our nurses, Lia and Jane, become baby-bird mothers for the summer.

All sorts of birds end up in the nursery. There are baby jackdaws, which look just like pterodactyls; fluffy owl babies who seem to be all feathers and two big blue eyes; baby ducks and a baby swan who live under a feather duster which they think of as mum, while five teeny blue tits live in an egg cup. There are lots of noisy baby starlings with thick yellow lips and cage after cage full of baby blackbirds who are brown until they grow up.

Bottle was brought to St. Tiggys by a little girl called Mandy. Mandy was crying because she thought that she had killed him.

Bottle was a naughty baby blackbird who had climbed out of his nest in a tree into a garden. He had tried to fly but his wings had not grown so he tumbled to the ground and, like a silly bird, walked off to explore.

He had walked such a long way, right across the park, that his parents could not find him. But Mandy Hoxton found him, luckily before one of the local cats had him for dinner!

Mandy bent down and picked him up. Bottle thought this was a good idea and opened his big yellow mouth and chirped as if to say, "I want some food."

Mandy put Bottle in the front pocket of her cardigan and ran all the way home holding the pocket so that he could not bounce out.

"Mum! Mum!" she shouted when she got home. "I've found this little bird in the park. I think he's an orphan. Can we give him something to eat?"

Mandy's mum was not pleased. "You shouldn't have picked him up. His mother and father will be looking for him."

But Bottle chirped even louder for food and jumped out of Mandy's hand across the table towards her mum.

"But, Mum," pleaded Mandy, "he was all on his own right out in the middle of the park." And even Mandy's mum could not resist such a little bird.

"Oh, all right," she said, "but how are we

going to feed him?"

Bottle opened his mouth even wider and chirped as if he was going to burst.

"I know," said Mandy. "I can use my little scent bottle to put the food right down the back of his throat."

"Let's try it," said her mum, "but if anything goes wrong we're going to take him to St. Tiggys."

Bottle was getting fed up with waiting and was getting quite angry. His latest chirping must have meant, "Come on, get on with it. I'm starving."

While her mum kept an eye on the baby blackbird, Mandy mixed some of her dog's tinned food with water to make it sloppy. Then with some of this mix in the scent bottle and the baby blackbird sitting on her left hand she tapped his beak.

He was starving, and in a flash opened his big mouth and grabbed at the food without giving Mandy a chance. He swallowed the food... and the scent bottle in one gulp! Mandy could not hold the slippery glass and before she knew it the bottle had disappeared down his throat. The tiny blackbird gulped and gurgled and swallowed it completely.

"Oh no," sobbed Mandy, "I think I've killed him. He's swallowed the whole bottle. He's going to die. I know he is."

"I knew there was going to be trouble," said Mandy's mum (as mums aways do!). "We'd better take him to St. Tiggys to see if they can do anything."

Mandy put the baby blackbird into one of her little doll's cots, with a teddy bear to keep him company, and ran out to the car still sobbing her eyes out.

Her mum drove quickly to St. Tiggywinkles and parked right up by the front door to save time.

Lia met them at the door and picked Bottle up to look at him. Bottle was still hungry and managed to open his big mouth to her and chirp,

"More food – please, please, please."

Mandy told Lia what had happened. "I was trying to feed him when he swallowed my perfume bottle," she said.

"He must have been very hungry," smiled Lia trying to cheer Mandy up. She looked down the blackbird's throat to see if she could see it. "Don't worry," she said, "I am sure Les can get it out without too much trouble. Leave him here but give us a ring in a couple of days and I'll let you know how he's getting on. Mandy, next time you find a baby bird, please bring it straight to us."

Lia carried the little bird down to the prep room where all newly arrived casualties are given first-aid care. The little blackbird sat down on its knees and looked just like a brown ball with black spots on its chest. Its big feet stuck out in front of it and we could clearly see the lump on its left side where the bottle was. He looked so low and sad that I fell for him straight away.

"Have you given him a name?" I asked Lia.

"Well, I thought I'd call him Bottle," she replied.

"Right," I said, "let's see if we can get this bottle out of Bottle."

Lia held the baby blackbird under the big light that helps us see the animals better. I took a long pair of tweezers, then opened Bottle's beak and very carefully put them right down the back of his throat. It all felt very soft and then I could feel something hard. It must be the bottle but it was a long way down, nearly into his stomach.

Carefully I prodded the hard lump with my tweezers until I think I felt the opening. I felt round and squeezed the tweezers on to the top of the bottle and slowly pulled it out. And then, just as I could clearly see its top, my tweezers slipped and it went down again. Bottle gulped and gurgled and swallowed it all over again.

Bottle did not seem to mind all this. In fact I think he thought he was being fed. He opened his beak and chirped for more.

I tried again and this time managed to hang on to the bottle and proudly waved it in front of Lia's nose.

"Got it," I grinned. "Now, young Bottle, let's settle you in the nursery."

Lia put Bottle in with a young thrush called Spot, who had also lost its parents. Bottle was still hungry and even begged food from Spot.

All baby birds beg for food by pushing their heads towards anybody who is likely to give it to them. They open their mouths wide and chirp loudly hoping that an adult bird will feed the open mouth. Spot, a thrush, looked nothing like an adult blackbird. He was a very light brown colour with a pale chest covered in dark black spots. But Bottle thought he was his mum! And Spot thought Bottle was his mum! They were both confused and must have forgotten what their real mums looked like. They soon learned that Lia was their new mum and she was the one who fed them.

In the fridge there were all sorts of baby

foods for all sorts of babies. There were wriggling maggots and mealworms for baby robins; there were special baby cereals for pigeons and big fat waxworms for swallows while the tins of puppy food were for the pterodactyls. Baby owls ate chopped-up mice while some of the waterbirds had tiny fish. Bottle was a blackbird and all blackbirds, thrushes and starlings were fed on St. Tiggywinkles Glop – lots of water, puppy food, dried insects and vitamins all mixed together to look like soft, brown ice cream.

When Bottle next opened that big mouth of his Lia shovelled in a big measure of sticky Glop. Bottle had hardly swallowed it when he opened his mouth chirping for more. Poor old Spot tried to get some but every time he opened his mouth Bottle would come barging in for more. Lia thought Bottle would burst. But after about six measures he closed his mouth. Then he lifted his bottom in the air and went to the toilet which meant he had had enough. So in the end even Spot got something to eat.

Spot was never as lucky as Bottle. When he jumped out of his nest he was caught by a cat and only just rescued in time. He was injured and had a big wound on his tummy which left his insides hanging out.

Luckily though, he was brought to St. Tiggys very quickly and we managed to give him an emergency operation that saved his life. He soon looked like a baby thrush again except that he had a bald tummy where we had to pull some feathers out. He also had a neat line of blue stitches where we had closed up the horrible wound. Like Bottle, Spot was not going to give up and as soon as he woke up after his operation he was shouting for food. He liked Glop and ate measure after measure. Then he stuck his bottom in the air and went to the toilet. We all cheered because this meant that he was going to be all right, too.

Bottle and Spot became good friends and stayed in the nursery for another two weeks. At night they would perch side by side, asleep with their heads tucked under their wings. But as soon as anyone touched their cage both mouths would come shooting out demanding food. As they grew older they started to hop round their cage investigating and pecking at every nook and cranny. Soon the two looked just like grown-up birds and Spot even had a few feathers over his tummy.

Now they were eating on their own. Breakfast was usually a nice bowl of wriggling maggots. So was lunch. In the evening they had a special treat of some mealworms and a few nice fat juicy waxworms – yummy! Everything a bird could want.

When they found out that they could fly, Lia put them outside in a big aviary with other young birds who had just learnt to fly and feed themselves. They had plenty of maggots, mealworms and waxworms to eat as well as a big, shallow bowl of water where they could bathe.

One warm sunny morning Matt went down and opened the end of the aviary and all the birds started to fly out into the trees around the hospital. Bottle did not even bother to say goodbye to Spot. He had found other young blackbirds and went off with them to look for tit-bits in the trees. Spot felt lost and alone. His one and only friend had flown off and he didn't know what to do. He wanted to fly after Bottle but something told him he was safer staying in the aviary. He sat for a very long time just inside the aviary door. Then he flew out... and flew straight back in again. He said to himself, "Why should I go out. I like it here. There's always plenty of food."

Then outside the aviary he saw something round and shiny over against a wall. It looked good to eat but he did not know what it was. He had never seen one of these in his life before and it looked nothing like the maggots he ate in the aviary. He was just about to fly over and see what it was when another thrush, a big one, flew down from a tree and pecked the round thing. Then as if to say 'watch me', the big thrush picked up the round thing in his beak and smashed it against a stone until it broke.

There was something soft and slimy inside that the thrush ate before it flew back into the trees. Spot looked along the wall and saw another round thing hidden by a brick. He flew over and just like the big thrush grabbed it and smashed it against a stone. Nothing happened. He tried again but the round thing just bounced off the stone. The big thrush had been watching Spot's efforts at breaking the round thing open and flew over to help. He chirped as if to say, "Here, watch me – these are snails and they are yummy." He picked up Spot's snail by the lip round the inside and flinging his head from side to side smashed the shell and left the inside for Spot to eat. Spot thought that snails tasted very good. So he followed the big thrush who showed him where there were lots more snails for them to eat. Spot forgot the aviary. He forgot

Bottle. He now had a new friend who knew where all the good food was to be found.

Bottle and his blackbird friends, and Spot with his new friend still live around St. Tiggys. Matt often throws them a few maggots as he goes off to feed the next aviary full of young birds.

Birds and animals that are fit and strong are always leaving St. Tiggywinkles and new patients who need our help are always arriving.

They all join the St. Tiggys family so that there will always be plenty of stories for me to tell!

Tips from St. Tiggywinkles

%   1.   Never pick up an animal or bird especially
      a baby unless it really does need rescuing.

%   2.   Never ever give bread and milk to
      hedgehogs or any other animal.

%   3.   Put out a shallow bowl of water in the
      garden so that blackbirds, thrushes and
      starlings can drink and bathe.

%   4.   Don't go near badgers, deer, foxes or swans.
      They can be very dangerous.

5. Keep your cat in at night. Unlike P. C. our domestic cats like to be in the warm and dry.

6. Never, ever run in the road to rescue an animal. Call a grown-up who will stop the traffic.

7. Always wash your hands after touching an animal or anything to do with an animal.

8. Make sure that if a hedgehog falls into your pond or swimming pool that it can climb out. If necessary put in a little ladder made from chicken wire.

9. Tell your mum or dad to check under bonfires before they light them or compost heaps before they shovel them up. There may be a hedgehog, mouse or grass snake family sleeping underneath.

If you would like further information on
St. Tiggywinkles, please send a stamped
and addressed envelope to

St. Tiggywinkles,
Aylesbury,
Bucks. HP17 8AF